MAKING THE GRADE *Toget*

EASY POPULAR DUETS FOR YOUNG PIANISTS. SELECTED AND ARRANGED BY LYNDA FRITH AND JERRY LANNING

Exclusive distributors:
Music Sales Limited
Newmarket Road, Bury St. Edmunds, Suffolk IP33 3YB.
This book © Copyright 1996 Chester Music.
Order No. CH61176
ISBN 0-7119-5866-1
Cover design by Pemberton & Whitefoord.
Printed in the United Kingdom by
Caligraving Limited, Thetford, Norfolk.

Chester Music

(A division of Music Sales Limited)
8/9 Frith Street, London W1V 5TZ.

INTRODUCTION

This collection of 11 popular duets has been carefully arranged to provide attractive repertoire for young pianists.

Generally, the technical demands of each part are equal, the standard progressing from approximately Grade 2 to Grade 4.

Some duets have one slightly harder part which a more experienced pupil or the teacher can play.

CONTENTS

Secondo

THE SKATER'S WALTZ

Composed by Emile Waldteufel

Play the bass notes firmly, and use a light *staccato* for the right hand chords.

Primo

THE SKATER'S WALTZ

Composed by Emile Waldteufel

The melody needs to be really *legato* in both hands. Make a slight break at the end of each phrase.

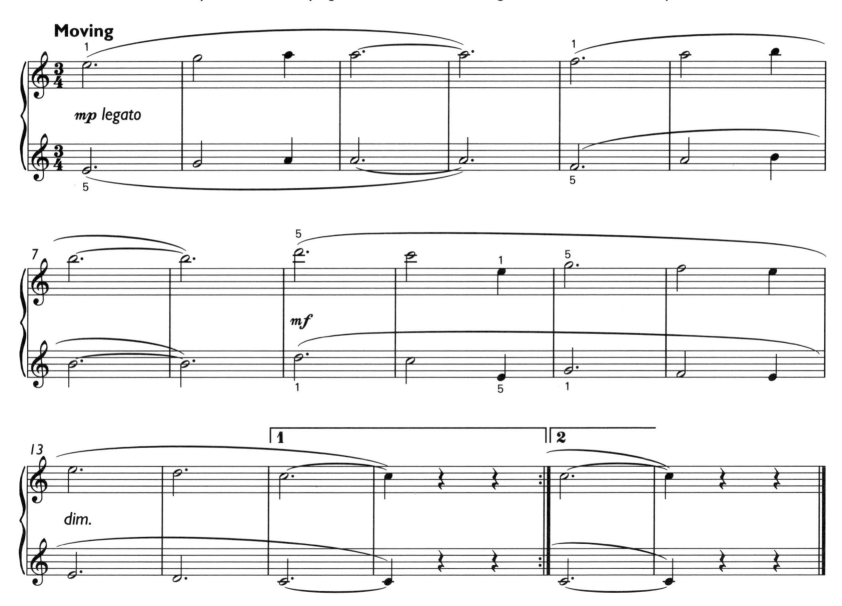

Secondo

HAVAH NAGILAH

Traditional

'Havah Nagilah' is a well-known traditional Jewish song.

Primo

HAVAH NAGILAH

Traditional

'Havah Nagilah' is a well-known traditional Jewish song. Notice that C sharp is
often followed by B flat (not B natural).

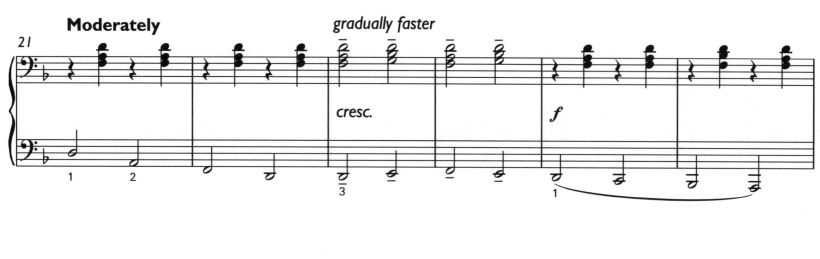

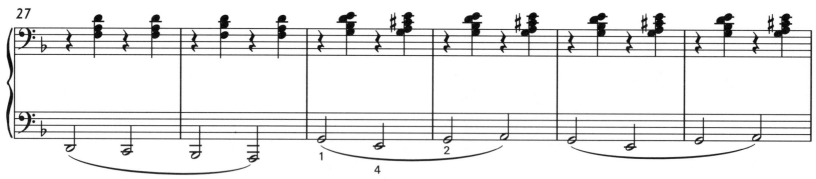

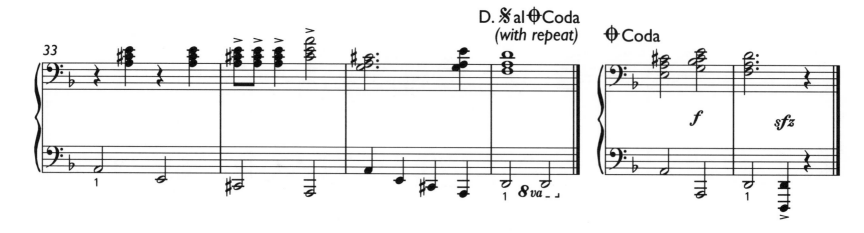

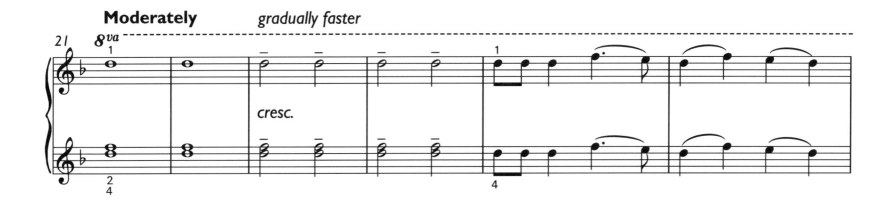

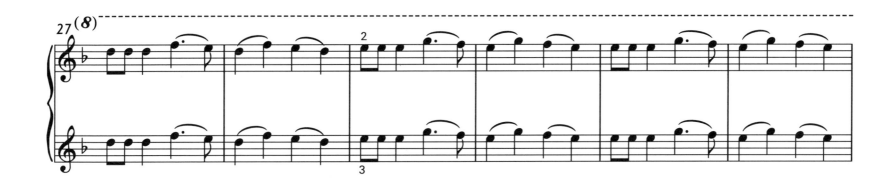

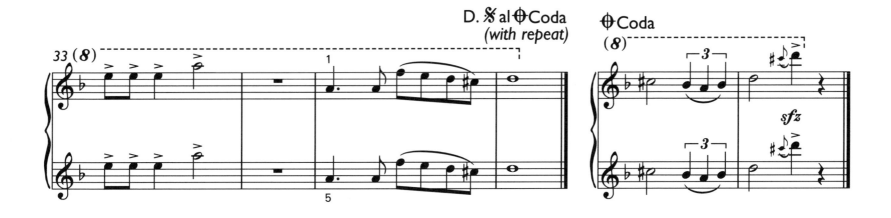

Secondo

COUNTRY GARDENS

Traditional

This very popular folk tune was originally a morris dance. Look out for the sudden
piano at bar ten, which creates an echo effect.

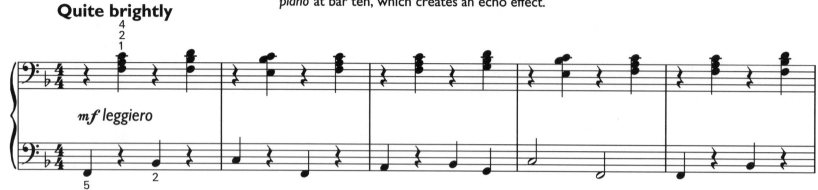

Primo
COUNTRY GARDENS

Traditional

This very popular folk tune was originally a morris dance. Look out for the sudden
piano at bar ten, which creates an echo effect.

Quite brightly

Secondo

YESTERDAY

Words & music by John Lennon & Paul McCartney

Keep a very steady tempo, with a clear and sustained bass line.

Moderately

YESTERDAY

Words & music by John Lennon & Paul McCartney

Notice the F and G sharps in the ascending scale of A melodic minor (bar two),
followed by F and G naturals in the descending scale.

Secondo

LOVE IS ALL AROUND

Words & music by Reg Presley

The tune passes between the two players, so careful observation of dynamics is very important.

With feeling

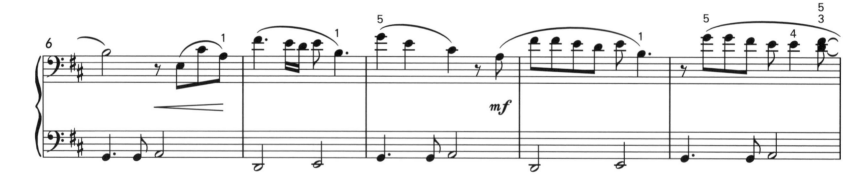

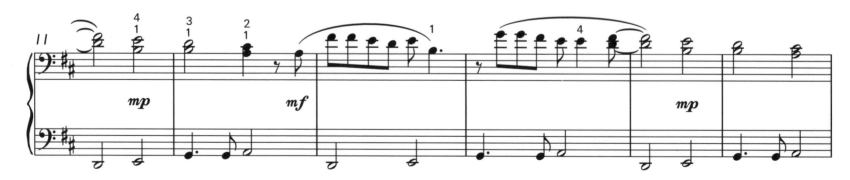

LOVE IS ALL AROUND

Words & music by Reg Presley

The tune passes between the two players, so careful observation of dynamics is very important.

With feeling

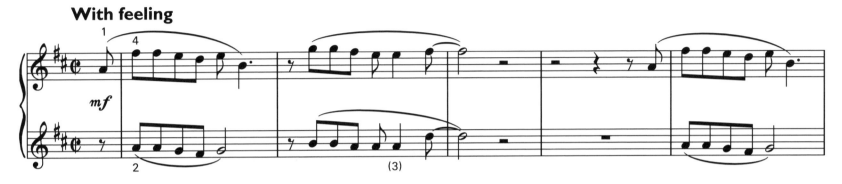

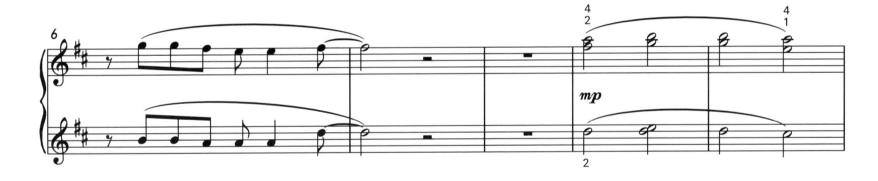

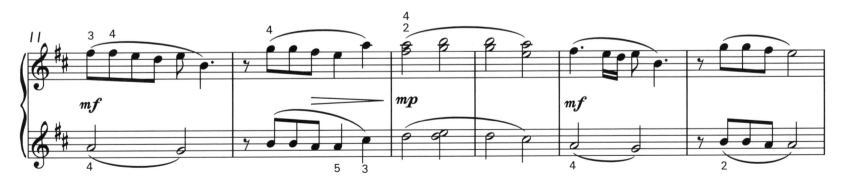

Secondo

Secondo

THE ENTERTAINER

By Scott Joplin

This piano rag featured in the film 'The Sting'. Keep a very steady tempo, thinking in
terms of four quavers rather than two crotchets in a bar.

Primo

THE ENTERTAINER

By Scott Joplin

This piano rag featured in the film 'The Sting'. Keep a very steady tempo, thinking in
terms of four quavers rather than two crotchets in a bar.

Not fast

Secondo

TO LOVE SOMEBODY

Words & music by Barry Gibb & Robin Gibb

The lower part has the melody most of the time. The upper part has a quieter off-beat accompaniment,
but notice the counter-melody from bar 9.

Primo

TO LOVE SOMEBODY

Words & music by Barry Gibb & Robin Gibb

The lower part has the melody most of the time. The upper part has a quieter off-beat accompaniment,
but notice the counter-melody from bar 9.

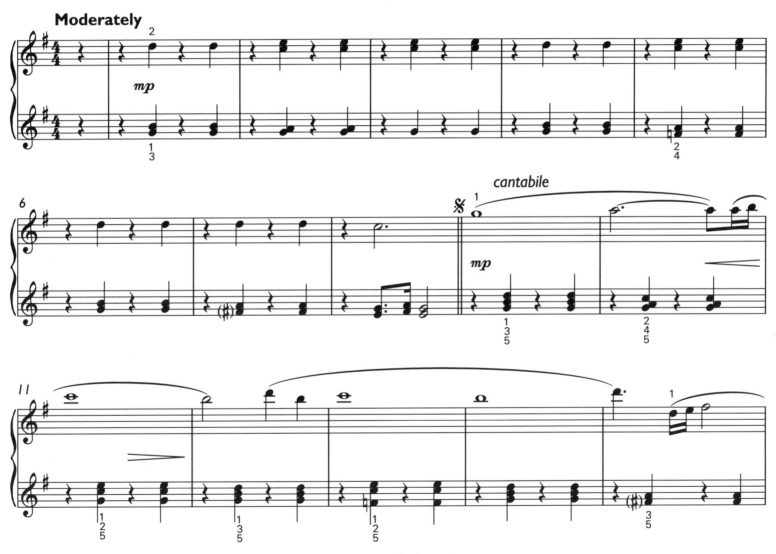

Secondo

FOOD GLORIOUS FOOD

Words & music by Lionel Bart

This is the opening chorus from the ever popular musical 'Oliver', based on the novel
'Oliver Twist' by Charles Dickens. It needs neat and accurate playing.

Primo

FOOD GLORIOUS FOOD

Words & music by Lionel Bart

This is the opening chorus from the ever popular musical 'Oliver', based on the novel
'Oliver Twist' by Charles Dickens. It needs neat and accurate playing.

Secondo

SHE'S OUT OF MY LIFE

Words & music Tom Bahler

Count very carefully, keeping a steady crotchet beat,
in order to keep the semiquavers and triplets in time.

SHE'S OUT OF MY LIFE

Words & music by Tom Bahler

Count very carefully, keeping a steady crotchet beat,
in order to keep the semiquavers and triplets in time.

Secondo

ASLAN'S THEME

Composed by Geoffrey Burgon

Keep a very smooth, sustained texture. The repeated quaver chords should not be *staccato*.

Moderately, with feeling

Primo

ASLAN'S THEME

Composed by Geoffrey Burgon

Make sure the melody projects clearly, even when it is only being played by the right hand.

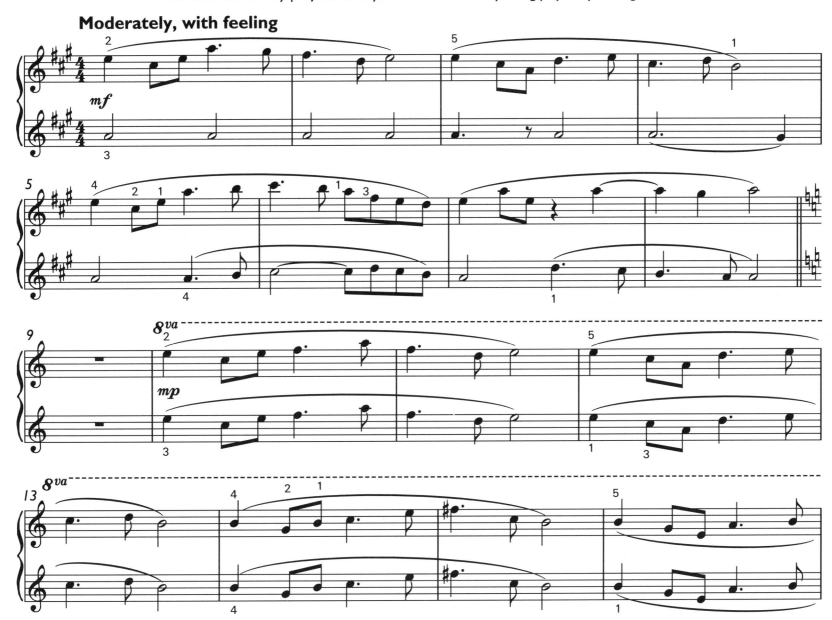

Secondo

Secondo

UNCHAINED MELODY

Music by Alex North, words by Hy Zaret

Notice the time signature and think in minims rather than crotchets.
Play as smoothly as possible throughout.

Moderately slow

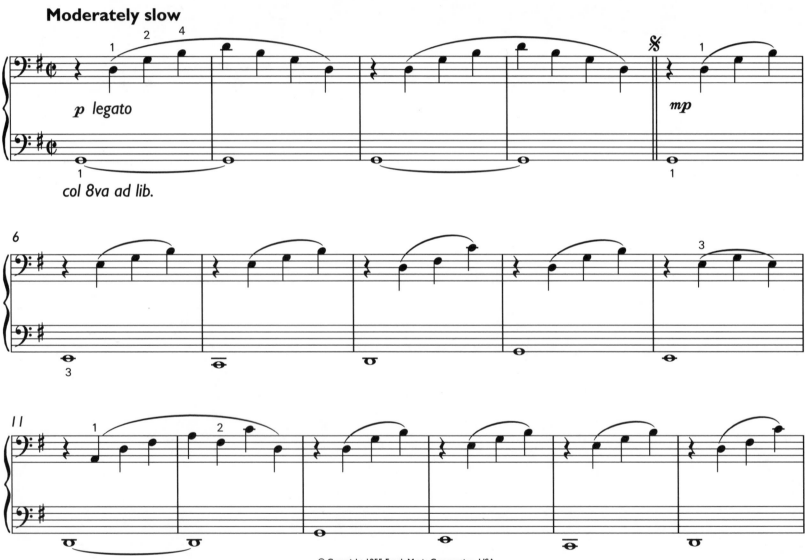

UNCHAINED MELODY

Music by Alex North, words by Hy Zaret

Notice the time signature and think in minims rather than crotchets.
Play as smoothly as possible throughout.

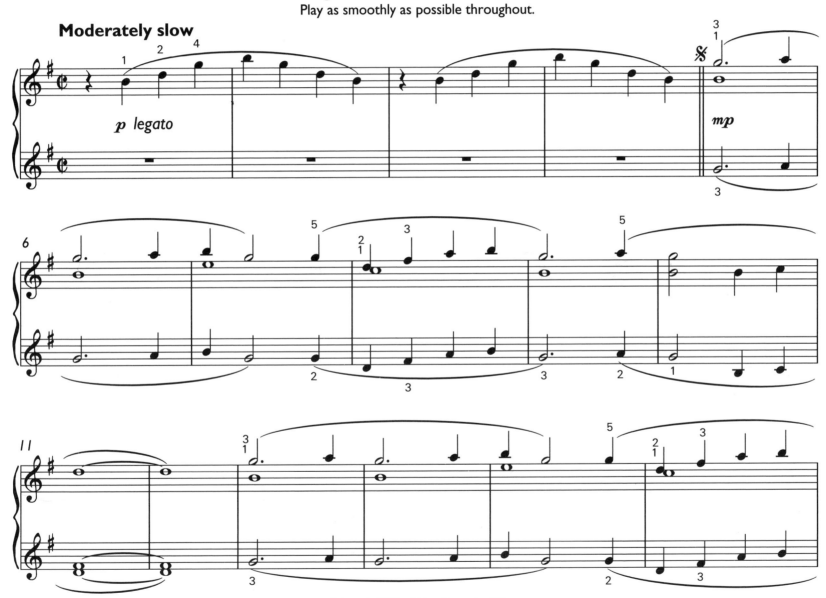